THE TALE OF
PETER RABBIT

Adapted from the story and art by Beatrix Potter
Line art by Lisa Wallace

S0-AWM-177

© 2014 Bendon. All rights reserved.
The BENDON name, logo, and Tear and Share are
trademarks of Bendon, Ashland, OH 44805.

Once upon a time there were four little Rabbits, and their
names were Flopsy, Mopsy, Cottontail, and Peter.

"My dears," said their mother one morning, "you may go into the
fields or down the lane, but don't go into Mr. McGregor's garden."

"Now run along, and don't
get into mischief. I am going out."

Then old Mrs. Rabbit took a basket and her umbrella,
and went through the woods to the baker's.

Flopsy, Mopsy, and Cottontail, who were good little bunnies,
went down the lane to gather blackberries. . .

. . .but Peter, who was very naughty, ran straight away to
Mr. McGregor's garden, and squeezed under the gate!

First he ate some lettuces and some French beans.
And then he ate some radishes.

And then, feeling rather sick, he went to look for some parsley.

But round the end of a cucumber frame,
whom should he meet but Mr. McGregor!

Mr. McGregor jumped up and ran after Peter,
waving a rake and calling out, "Stop, thief."

Peter was dreadfully frightened. He rushed all over the garden,
for he had forgotten the way back to the gate.
He lost both of his shoes!

After losing them, he ran on four legs and went faster,
so that I think he might have got away altogether
if he had not unfortunately run into a gooseberry net.

He got caught by the large buttons on his jacket.
Peter gave himself up for lost, and shed big tears. His sobs were
overheard by some friendly sparrows.

Mr. McGregor came up to catch Peter, but Peter wriggled out
just in time, leaving his jacket behind him.

Peter rushed into the toolshed and jumped into a can—full of water!

Mr. McGregor searched all through the toolshed.
Suddely, Peter sneezed—"Kertyschoo!"

Mr. McGregor was after him in no time!

Peter hopped and hopped until Mr. Mcgregor grew tired of running.
Peter began to wander about, going lippity—lippity—not very fast,
and looking all around.

He found a door in a wall, but it was locked, and there was no
room for a fat little rabbit to squeeze underneath.

An old mouse was running in and out over the stone doorstep.
Peter asked her the way to the gate, but she had such a
large pea in her mouth that she could not answer.

Then Peter tried to find his way straight across the garden.
He came to a pond where Mr. McGregor filled his watering cans.
A white cat was staring at some goldfish.
She sat very, very still.

Peter went back toward the toolshed. Suddenly, he heard
the noise of a hoe—scr-r-ritch, scratch, scratch, scritch.
It was Mr. McGregor. And there beyond him was the gate!

Peter started running as fast as he could go toward the gate!
Peter slipped underneath the gate, and was safe
at last in the woods outside the garden.

Mr. McGregor hung up the little jacket and the shoes
as a scarecrow to frighten the blackbirds.

Peter never stopped running till he got home to the big fir tree.
He was so tired that he flopped down upon the nice soft sand on the floor
of the rabbit hole and shut his eyes.

His mother was busy cooking.
She wondered what he had done with his clothes.

I am sorry to say that Peter was not very well during the evening.

His mother put him to bed,
and made some camomile tea; and she gave a dose of it to Peter:
"One tablespoonful to be taken at bedtime."

But Flopsy, Mopsy, and Cottontail
had bread and milk and blackberries for supper.

THE END

From the World of
Beatrix Potter

Jeremy Fisher

TOM KITTEN

MRS. TIGGY-WINKLE

THE TALE OF
BENJAMIN BUNNY

Adapted from the story and art by Beatrix Potter
Line art by Lisa Wallace

One morning, little Benjamin Bunny sat on a bank.
He heard the trit-trot of Mr. McGregor's carriage.

So, Mr. McGregor was leaving for town! With a hop,
skip, and a jump, Benjamin Bunny set off down the path.

The wood was full of rabbit holes. In the neatest, sandiest hole lived
Benjamin's Aunt and his cousins—Flopsy, Mopsy, Cottontail, and . . .

. . . Peter! But Peter was not at home in the rabbit hole.
Benjamin went looking for him.

Benjamin came round the back of a tree.

Benjamin found Peter dressed in a pocket-handkerchief,
for he had lost his clothes in Mr. McGregor's garden.

Little Benjamin sat down beside his cousin
and told him that Mr. McGregor had gone to town.

And where do you think those two little rabbits set off to?

Mr. McGregor's garden! And there they
saw Peter's coat and shoes on a scarecrow.

Rather than squeeze under the gate, the two cousins
climbed down a pear tree—but poor Peter tumbled down!

They left many little footprints in the soft lettuce bed.

Peter took his clothes from the scarecrow and put them on.
Benjamin tried on the tam-o'-shanter, but it was too big for him.

Benjamin filled the pocket-handkerchief
with onions, as a little present for his Aunt.

Peter did not seem to be enjoying himself.
He kept hearing noises.

But Benjamin said he was in the habit of
coming to the garden with his father to get lettuces.
And the lettuces certainly were very fine.

Peter did not eat anything. He wanted to go home.
Soon he had dropped half the onions.

Benjamin led the way to the other side of the garden. Little mice
sat on their doorsteps cracking seeds and winking at the bunnies.

Presently Peter let the pocket-handkerchief go again.

The cousins got among the flower pots and Peter heard noises!
Suddenly he stopped!

This is what those little rabbits saw around the corner!

In no time at all, little Benjamin and Peter
hid underneath a large basket.

The cat got up, sniffed, and sat right down on top of the basket.
She sat there for *five hours*.

Pitter-patter, pitter patter. Mr. Benjamin Bunny
was on the wall above the shed looking for his son.

Mr. Benjamin Bunny was not afraid of cats.
He pounced onto that cat and kicked it into the greenhouse!

He lifted the basket and got his son Benjamin and his nephew Peter.

Then Mr. Benjamin Bunny marched
those two naughty bunnies out of the garden.

Mr. McGregor returned and thought:
Where did the scarecrow's clothes go?

When Peter got home, his mother forgave him,
because she was so glad to see that he had found his shoes and coat.

THE END